children's
holiday
songbook

Arranged by GARY LERNER
Edited by PETER FOSS
First Published 1988
© International Music Publications

Exclusive Distributors
International Music Publications
Southend Road, Woodford Green,
Essex IG8 8HN, England.

215-2-517

Leaving On A Jet Plane

Words and Music
by JOHN DENVER

4

3. Now the time has come to leave you,
   One more time let me kiss you,
   Then close your eyes I'll be on my way.
   Dream about the days to come
   When I won't have to leave alone,
   About the times I won't have to say:
   CHORUS

April In Portugal

Words by JIMMY KENNEDY
Music by RAUL FERRAO

California Here I Come

Words and Music by AL JOLSON,
BUD DE SYLVA and JOSEPH MEYER

9

From Russia With Love

Words and Music
by LIONEL BART

How Are Things In Glocca Morra

Words by E Y HARBURG
Music by BURTON LANE

I Belong To Glasgow

Words and Music
by WILL FYFFE

I Left My Heart In San Francisco

Words by DOUGLASS CROSS
Music by GEORGE CORY

Island In The Sun

Words and Music by
HARRY BELEFONTE and LORD BURGESS

New York, New York

Words by FRED EBB
Music by JOHN KANDER

Moderately, with rhythm

Start spread-in' the news, I'm leav-ing to-day, I wan-na be a part—of it, New York, New York. These vag-a-bond shoes

I'll make a brand new start— of it in old New York. If I can make it there, — I'd make it an - y-where, — It's up to you, New York, New York.

1. York. Start spreadin' the

2. York.

The Last Time I Saw Paris

Words by OSCAR HAMMERSTEIN II
Music by JEROME KERN

Londonderry Air (Danny Boy)

TRADITIONAL

2. But when ye come, and all the flowers are dying,
   If I am dead, as dead I well may be,
   Ye'll come and find the place where I am lying,
   And kneel and say an Ave there for me;
   And I shall hear, though soft you tread above me,
   And all my grave will warmer, sweeter be,
   For you will bend and tell me that you love me,
   And I shall sleep in peace until you come to me.

Poppa Piccolino

Italian Words by RASTELLI and PANZERI
English Lyrics by BOB MUSEL
Music by MASCHERONI

The Rain In Spain

Words by ALAN JAY LERNER
Music by FREDERICK LOEWE

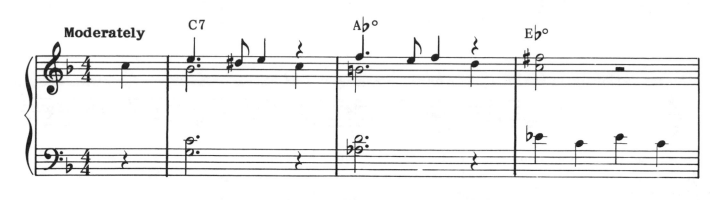

The rain in Spain stays main-ly in the plain.

The rain in Spain stays

main-ly in the plain.——— Now once a-

Chappell & Co Inc, Publisher and owner of allied rights throughout the world
Chappell Music Ltd, London W1Y 3FA

The Road To Morocco

Words by JOHNNY BURKE
Music by JIMMY VAN HEUSEN

The Skye Boat Song

TRADITIONAL

Tulips From Amsterdam

Words by NEUMANN and BADER
English Lyrics by GENE MARTYN
Music by RALF ARNIE

Valencia

Words by LUCIEN BOYER and JACQUES CHARLES
English Lyrics by ERIC VALENTINE
Music by JOSE PADILLA

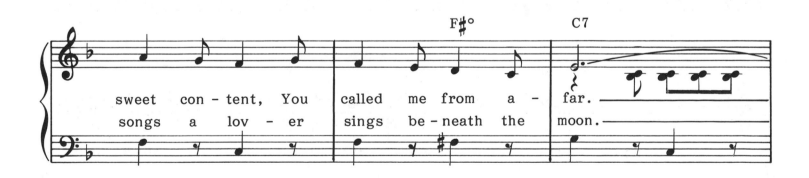

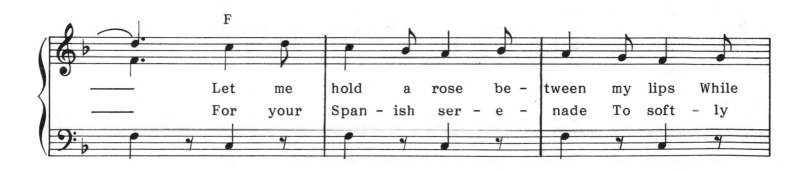

48

A Windmill In Old Amsterdam

Words and Music by
TED DICKS and MYLES RUDGE

4 verses (last verse "The daughters got married ———— when no one was listening

CHORUS

Liv - ing in a wind - mill in old Am - ster - dam!" *slight rall.*

I saw a mouse. Where? There on a stair. Where on a stair? Right there! A lit - tle mouse with clogs on,

Well I de - clare, Go - ing clip clip - pe - ty clop on the stair.

Oh, yeah! 2.The yeah! 4.The

52

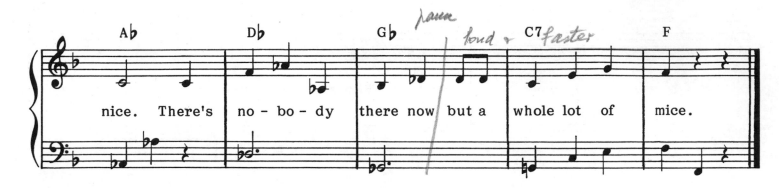

2. The mouse he got lonesome he took him a wife,
   A windmill with mice in is hardly surprisin'.
   She sang every morning,
   "How lucky I am,
   Living in a windmill in old Amsterdam!"
   CHORUS

3. First they had triplets and then they had quins,
   A windmill with quins in - triplets and twins in.
   They sang every morning,
   "How lucky we are,
   Living in a windmill in Amsterdam, ya!"
   CHORUS

4. The daughters got married and so did the sons,
   The windmill had christenings when no-one was listening.
   They all sang in chorus,
   "How lucky we are,
   Living in a windmill in Amsterdam, ya!"
   CHORUS

Under The Bridges Of Paris

Words by J RODOR
English Lyrics by DORCAS COCHRAN
Music by VINCENT SCOTTO

We'll Keep A Welcome

Words by LYN JOSHUA and JAMES HARPER
Music by MAI JONES

*Hee-rythe: (<u>longing</u> or <u>yearning</u>)

The White Rose Of Athens

Words by NORMAN NEWELL
Additional Words by ARCHIE BLEYER
Music by MANOS HADJIDAKIS

Wonderful Copenhagen

Words and Music
by FRANK LOESSER

Hometown

Words and Music by
J KENNEDY and M CARR

Printed by Watkiss Studios Ltd., Biggleswade, Beds. 5/89